HOME #1
IGHTER THAN AIR

UBLE TAKE

$2.50   COAST | ROWE | CATALANO | JEMAS | MELEK

ULTIMATE
Cocktail Party

Sidecar
3/4 ounce triple sec
3/4 ounce lemon juice
1 1/2 ounces cognac

Martini
2 1/2 ounces dry gin
1/2 ounce dry vermouth
Green olive for garnish

Classic Onion Dip

Ingredients
1 ½ cups of chopped onion
½ cup of mayonnaise
3 tbsps of butter
1 tsp of black pepper
¼ tsp of salt
2 cups of sour cream
1 tsp of garlic powder

Directions:
· Heat butter in a saucepan. Add black pepper, salt, garlic powder and onions, sauté for 10 minutes.
· Mix mayonnaise, sour cream and sautéed onions in large bowl. Serve at room temperature or chilled if desired.

Manhattan
2 ounces bourbon whiskey
1/2 ounce sweet vermouth
1/2 ounce dry vermouth
2 dashes Angostura bitters
Maraschino cherry

Cosmo
2 ounces vodka
1/2 ounce triple sec
3/4 ounce cranberry juice
1/4 ounce fresh lime juice
1 2-inch orange peel/twist

Swiss Fondue

Ingredients
2 cups of shredded Emmental (or Swiss) cheese
2 cups of shredded Gruyere cheese
3 tbsps cornstarch
1 clove of garlic, minced
1 tsp of ground mustard
1 cup of dry white wine
1 tablespoon of lemon juice
Pinch of nutmeg
Assorted dipping foods

Directions:
· Mix Emmental, Gruyere, cornstarch, and ground mustard into large bowl.
· Add wine, garlic, and lemon juice into a saucepan. Bring to a boil over medium heat.
· Begin adding cheese mixture, stirring in between additions. Add pinch of nutmeg. Fondue is done when cheese is melted and mixture has a smooth texture.
· Transfer fondue to a fondue pot.
· Arrange dipping foods around fondue pot and serve.

Deviled Eggs

Ingredients
6 eggs
2 tablespoons of mayonnaise
1 teaspoon of yellow mustard
Salt and black pepper to taste
Paprika

Directions:
· Hard boil eggs and slice into halves.
· Separate yolks from egg whites and place yolks in a bowl.
· Mash yolks using a fork. Add mayonnaise, mustard, salt, and pepper and stir.
· Spoon mixture into egg whites using a teaspoon. Sprinkle paprika to garnish.
· Chill eggs for 1 hour and serve.

"I've been trying to eat more vegans."

STORY
MICHAEL COAST
JULIAN ROWE
ERIC HOBBS
BILL JEMAS

SCRIPT
MICHAEL COAST

LAYOUTS
JULIAN ROWE

PENCILS
MONICA CATALANO
FERNANDO MELEK

COLORS
JAVIER MENA

COVER
JULIAN ROWE

LETTERS
CAROLINE FLANAGAN

EDITORS
ELYSIA LIANG
CLAIRE DRANGINIS

DOUBLE TAKE

RICHARD BROOKS | PRODUCTION ASSISTANT
MICHAEL COAST | STORY EDITOR
CLAIRE DRANGINIS | PRODUCTION COORDINATOR
CAROLINE FLANAGAN | PRODUCTION ASSISTANT
ALLISON GADSDEN | EDITORIAL INTERN
WILLIAM GRAVES | DIGITAL PRODUCTION ARTIST
CHARLOTTE GREENBAUM | EDITORIAL ASSISTANT

YOUNG HELLER | STORYBOARD ILLUSTRATOR
BILL JEMAS | GENERAL MANAGER
ELYSIA LIANG | EDITORIAL ASSISTANT
ROBERT MEYERS | MANAGING EDITOR
JULIAN ROWE | STORYBOARD ILLUSTRATOR
LILLIAN TAN | BUSINESS MANAGER
GABE YOCUM | SALES & MARKETING COORDINATOR

Sunday, April 24, 1966, 6:00 pm
Evans County, Pennsylvania

Colossians! I know it well, sir.

Good evening. Tom O'Brien reporting on the news as of this moment, brought to you in color on the weekend report.

Project officials report tonight a short circuit in Gemini's vital maneuvering rocket system caused the violent rollovers.

Coming up: information on the returning Venus Probe, shot down by NASA last night due to high levels of radiation.

Kevin? Find your sister, and you two clean yourselves up for dinner.

Okay, Mom. In a minute.

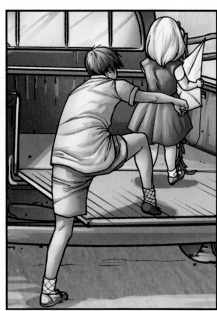

All set back there?

Ready for liftoff, mission control!

Boy! I can't wait to blast off into new galaxies.

You pretend the truck is a spaceship and I'll pretend you died in the womb.

T-minus 5...4...3...2...1... And ignition!

You're the prettiest girl I've ever seen, Linda.

Don't tell me how you feel. Show me.

Let's just take this off.

Tim! Linda! Can you come down, please?

Dad's a real Forgetful Frank sometimes.

Sounds like they need a push.

I bet you never been laid before.

You think you're getting into my sister's pants? She's not that easy.

Dry d#ck motherf#cker.

Can you survive the zombie apocalypse?

Yes? You probably think you can.

There is only one way to find out.

Play the **Dead Reign® RPG**. The core rule book, a few players, some dice and an active imagination are all you need to start playing. Rules are easy. Character creation is fast and fun. Combat, quick and deadly. Survival? Harder than you may think.

- **7 different types of zombies. Zombie combat and survival tips.**
- **6 Apocalyptic Character Classes and Ordinary People.**
- **101 Random Scenarios, Encounters, Settings and places of note.**
- **100 Random Corpse Searches, other tables, weapons & vehicles.**
- **Death Cults, their Priests, power over zombies and goals.**
- **Quick Roll Character Creation tables (10 minutes).**
- **5 sourcebooks provide more types of zombies, survival tips, new dangers and adventure.**
- **The Dead Reign™ core rule book is 224 pages – Cat. No. 230. A complete role-playing game book.**

Discover the Palladium Books® RPG Megaverse®

Fun to read. A blast to play. The Palladium role-playing rule system is the same in every game. This means once readers become familiar with one game, they can play them *ALL*.

Better yet, you can link and combine several game worlds to create epic, multi-dimensional adventures on a cosmic scale!

What's that? You've never seen a role-playing game? The role-playing core rule book contains all the rules and data you need to create characters and get you started. Each game or supplement is a magazine size soft-bound or hardcover book, 48-352 pages, and jam-packed with great art, heroes, villains, adventure and tons of ideas. **Dead Reign®** and **Robotech®** are excellent for those of you new to pen and paper RPGs.

Rifts® is the Earth of the future, but a transformed and alien Earth where magic and technology coexist and realities from countless dimensions collide. Alien predators and supernatural monsters prey upon the human survivors and threaten to conquer the world.

Players can be any number of aliens, mutants, warriors, cyborgs, robots and wizards. Lines of magic crisscross the Earth, giving life to dragons, godlings and supernatural horrors. They also lead to dimensional gateways called "Rifts" that link the Earth to the infinite Megaverse®. In **Rifts®** anything is possible.

Unleash your imagination! Drop by our website to learn more about our games or make purchases from our online store. Also available in comic book and game stores everywhere.

www.palladiumbooks.com

DISCOVER THE LARGEST INDEPENDENT SUPERHERO UNIVERSE
IN COMICS | EACH VOLUME ONE ONLY $9.99

THE VALIANT

**X-O MANOWAR
VOL. 1: BY THE SWORD**

**BLOODSHOT REBORN
VOL. 1: COLORADO**

**HARBINGER
VOL. 1: OMEGA RISING**

DIVINITY

**QUANTUM AND WOODY
VOL. 1: THE WORLD'S WORST
SUPERHERO TEAM**

**THE DEATH-DEFYING
DR. MIRAGE**

**RAI
VOL. 1: WELCOME TO NEW JAPAN**

**NINJAK
VOL. 1: WEAPONEER**

**ARCHER & ARMSTRONG
VOL. 1: THE MICHELANGELO CODE**

**IVAR, TIMEWALKER
VOL. 1: MAKING HISTORY**

**IMPERIUM
VOL. 1: COLLECTING MONSTER**

Kevin and Lisa. I bet I know what you guys want. Liver and onions?

Very f#cking funny. Ice cream. Now.

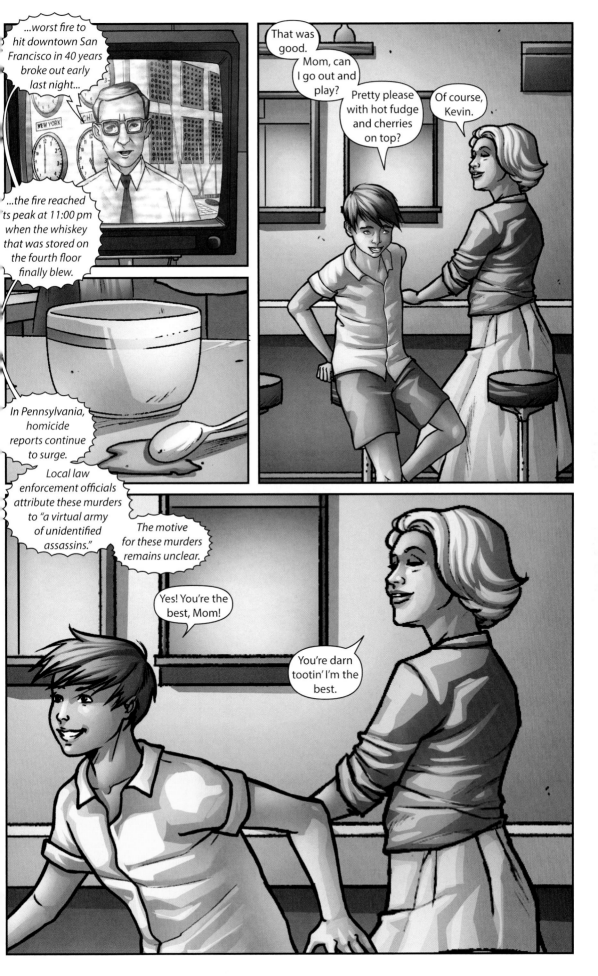

God damn, pie. I will eat the sh#t out of you.

Uh, excuse me. A##hole.

Someone is standing here.

Oh. You did *not* just do that.

Now come on, let's put that down.

Why don't you just come—

That's enough of this.

That f#cker attacked me! You going to just stand here and let your kid get assaulted?

Watch out, he's kicking!

Sorry about that, folks. Coffee on the house.